The Piano Songbook

Nina Simone

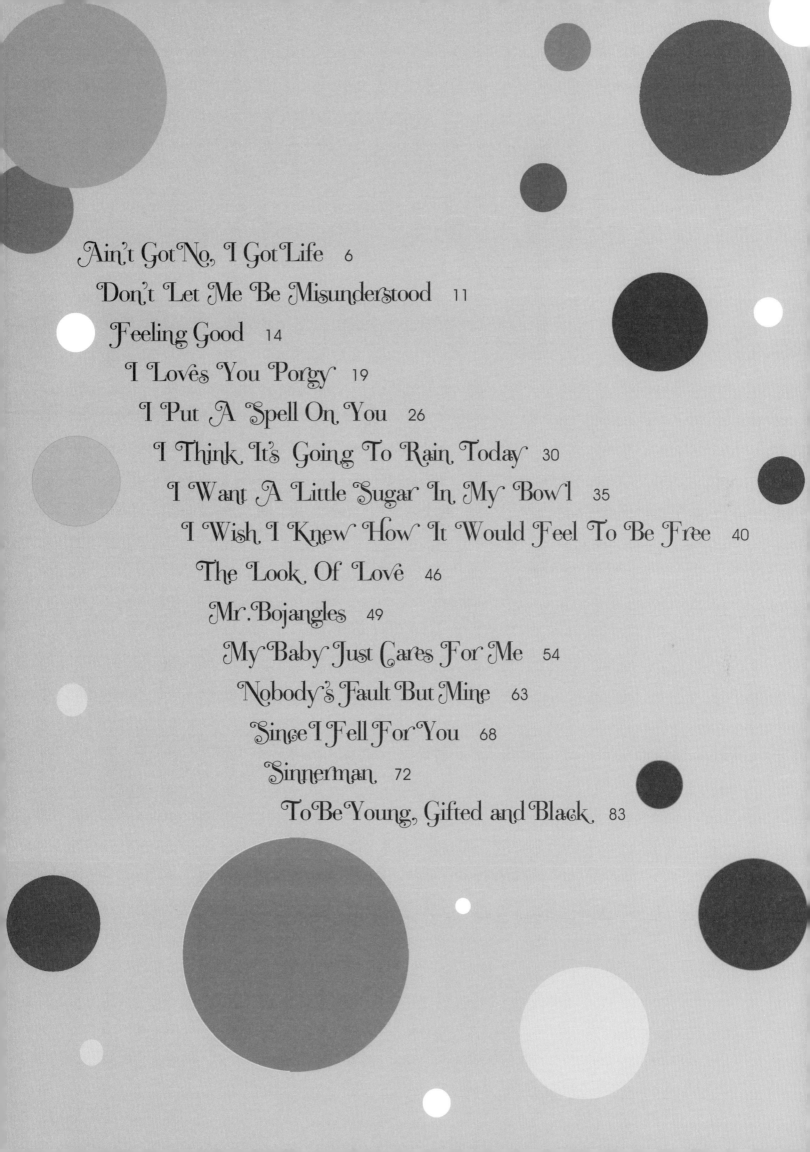

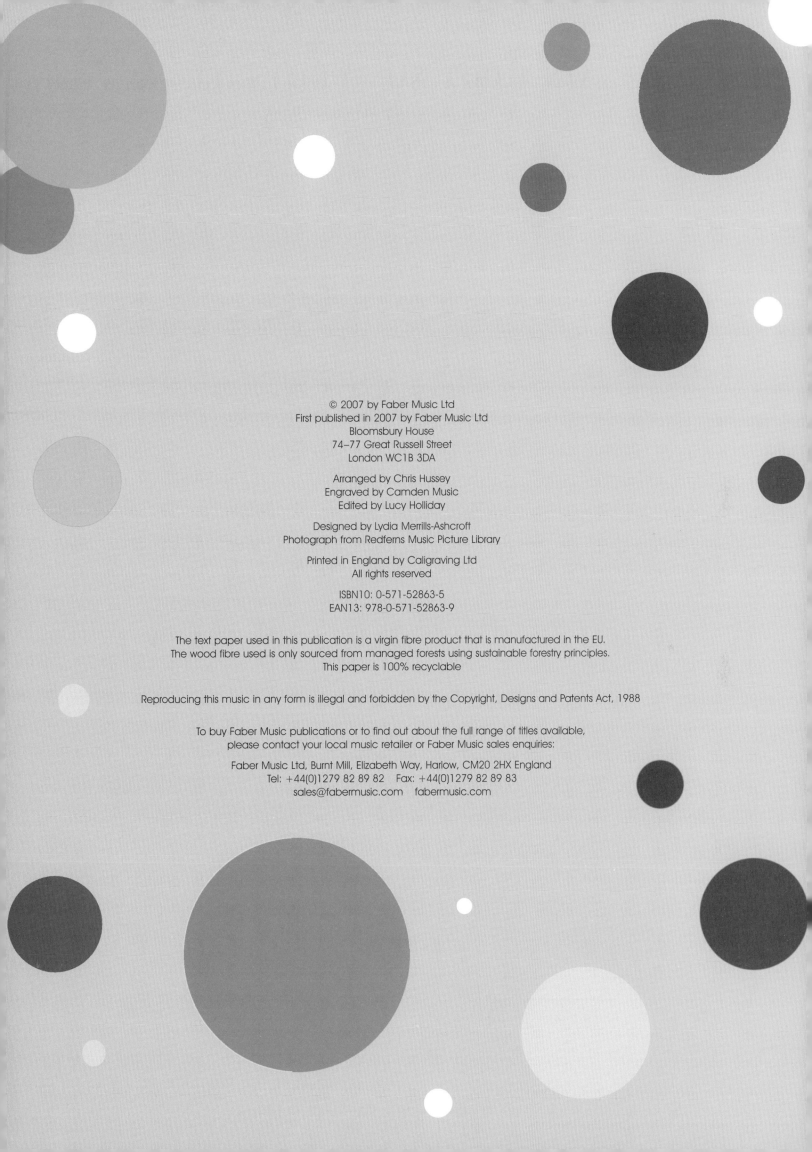

© 2007 by Faber Music Ltd
First published in 2007 by Faber Music Ltd
Bloomsbury House
74–77 Great Russell Street
London WC1B 3DA

Arranged by Chris Hussey
Engraved by Camden Music
Edited by Lucy Holliday

Designed by Lydia Merrills-Ashcroft
Photograph from Redferns Music Picture Library

Printed in England by Caligraving Ltd
ISBN10: 0-571-52863-5
EAN13: 978-0-571-52863-9

The text paper used in this publication is a virgin fibre product that is manufactured in the EU.
The wood fibre used is only sourced from managed forests using sustainable forestry principles.
This paper is 100% recyclable

To buy Faber Music publications or to find out about the full range of titles available,
please contact your local music retailer or Faber Music sales enquiries:

Faber Music Ltd, Burnt Mill, Elizabeth Way, Harlow, CM20 2HX England
Tel: +44(0)1279 82 89 82   Fax: +44(0)1279 82 89 83
sales@fabermusic.com   fabermusic.com

AIN'T GOT NO – I GOT LIFE

Words by James Rado and Gerome Ragni
Music by Galt MacDermot

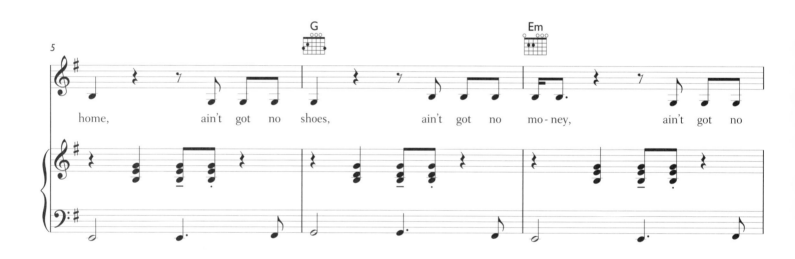

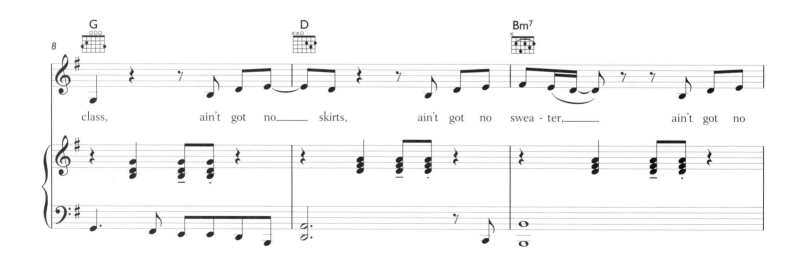

DON'T LET ME BE MISUNDERSTOOD

Words and Music by Bennie Benjamin, Sol Marcus and Gloria Caldwell

FEELING GOOD

Words and Music by Leslie Bricusse and Anthony Newley

Birds fly-ing high, you know how I feel. Sun in the sky, you know how I feel.

Breeze drift-ing on by, you know how I feel. It's a new dawn, it's a new day,

it's a new life for me, yeah. It's a new dawn, it's a new day, it's a new life for me.

Ooh. And I'm feel - ing good.

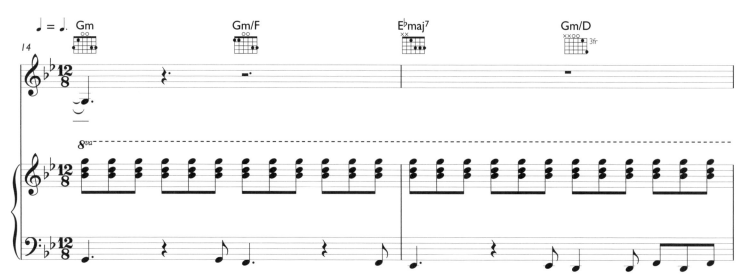

I LOVES YOU PORGY

Music and Lyrics by George Gershwin, Du Bose Heyward, Dorothy Heyward and Ira Gershwin

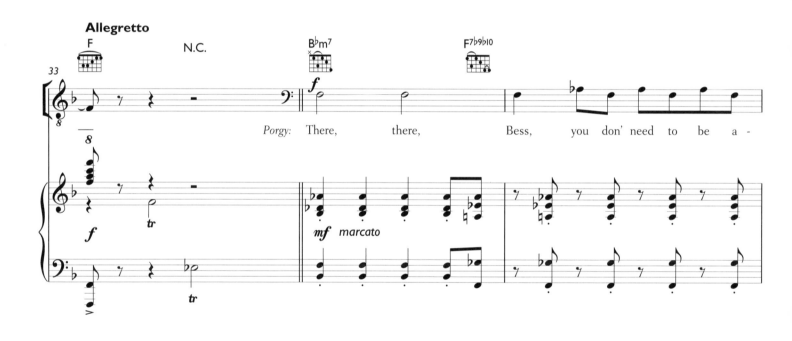

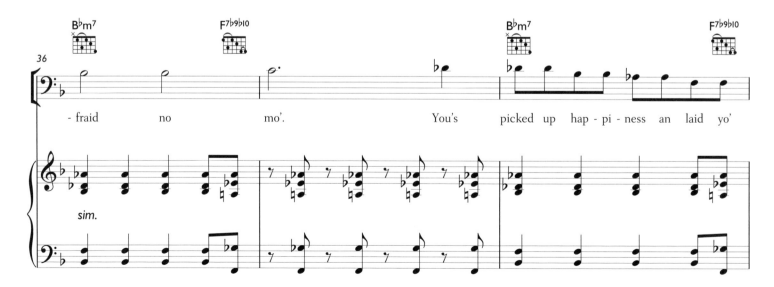

I PUT A SPELL ON YOU

Words and Music by Jay Hawkins

I THINK IT'S GOING TO RAIN TODAY

Words and Music by Randy Newman

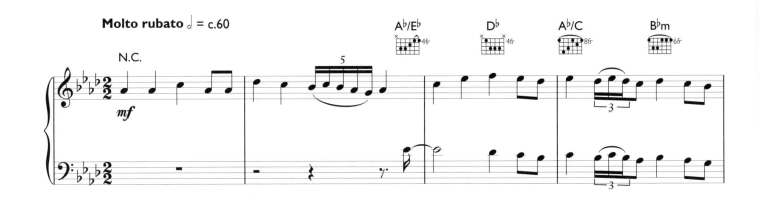

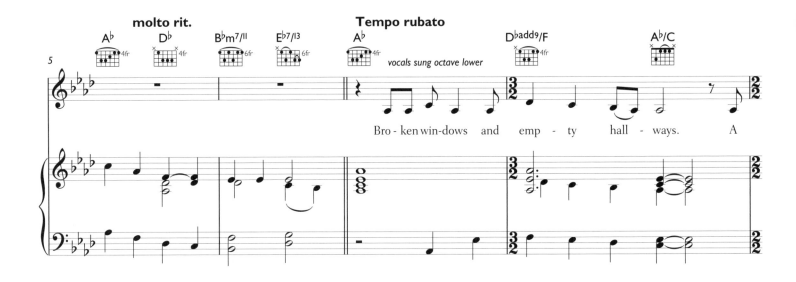

Bro - ken win-dows and emp - ty hall - ways. A

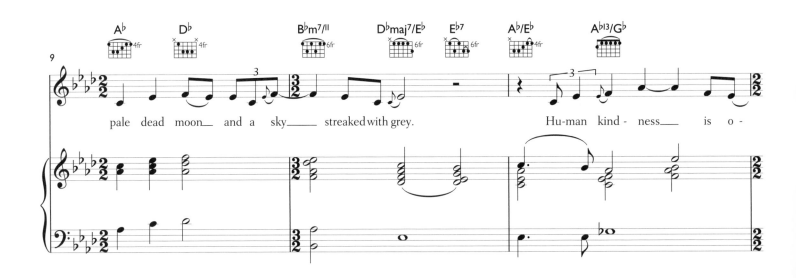

pale dead moon___ and a sky___ streaked with grey.   Hu-man kind - ness___ is o-

I WANT A LITTLE SUGAR IN MY BOWL

Words and Music by Tim Brymn, Danny Small and Clarence Williams

Original key: B major

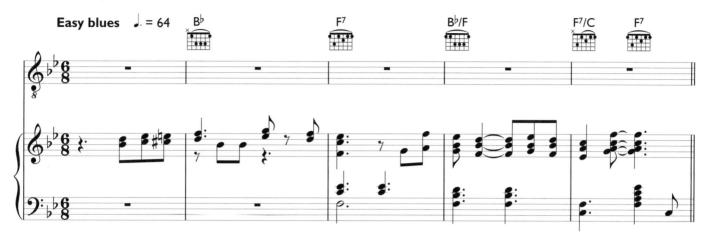

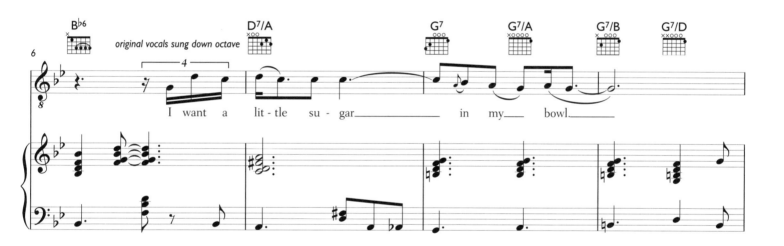

I want a lit-tle su-gar _____ in my _____ bowl. _____

I wan-na lit-tle sweet-ness _____ down ____ in my soul. _____

38

I WISH I KNEW HOW IT WOULD FEEL TO BE FREE

Words and Music by Dick Dallas and Billy Taylor

THE LOOK OF LOVE

Words by Hal David
Music by Burt Bacharach

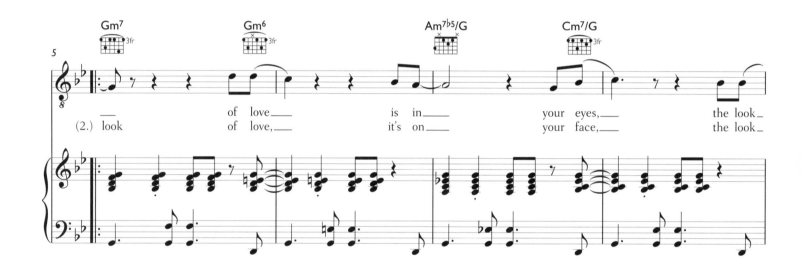

MR BOJANGLES

Words and Music by Jerry Jeff Walker

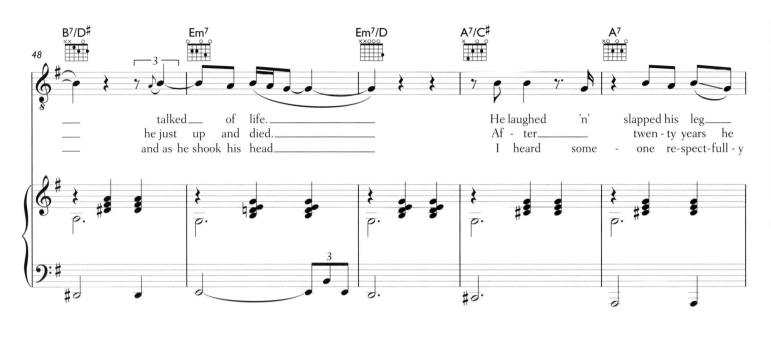

talked__ of life._____
he just up and died._____
and as he shook his head_____

He laughed 'n' slapped his leg__
Af - ter_____ twen - ty years he
I heard some - one re-spect-full - y

a step.
still grieved.
ask "please"...

Mis-ter Bo -

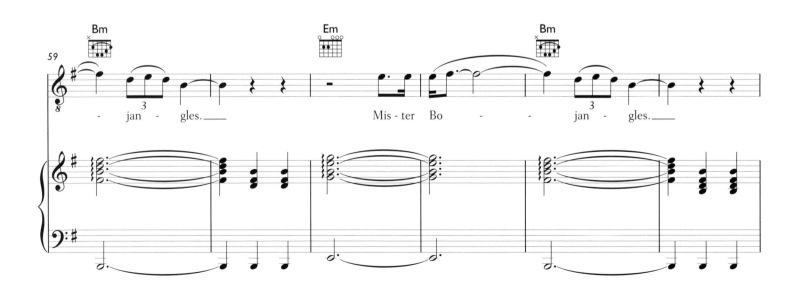

- jan - gles.____ Mis - ter Bo - jan - gles.____

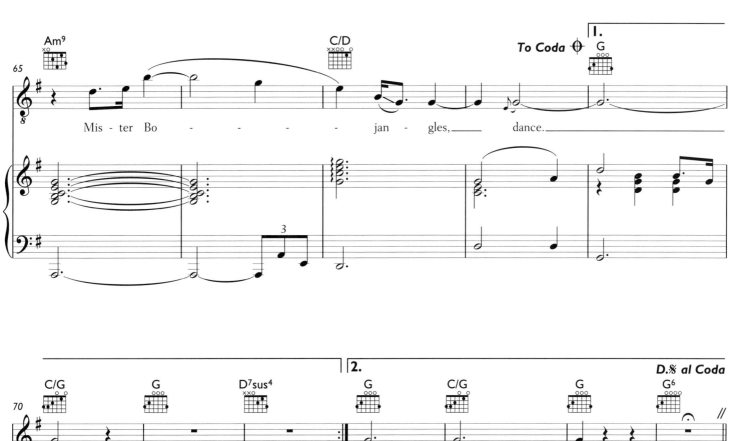

Mis - ter Bo - - - - - jan - gles,____ dance._____

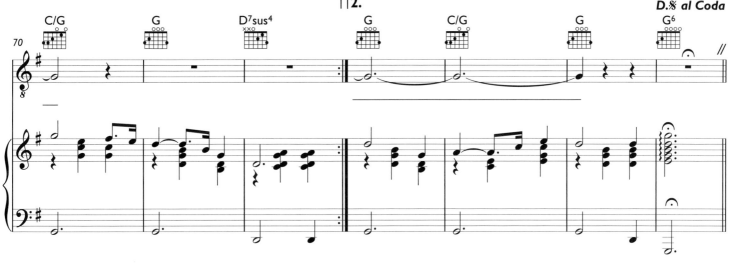

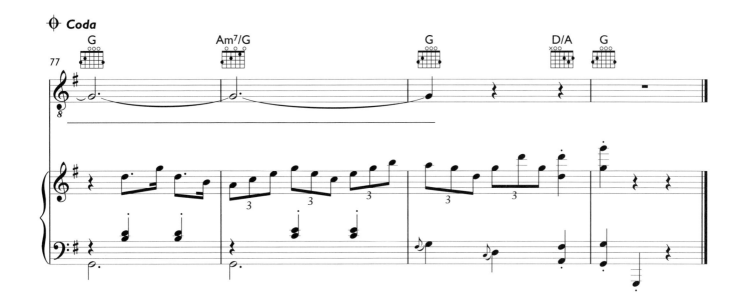

MY BABY JUST CARES FOR ME

Words by Gus Kahn
Music by Walter Donaldson

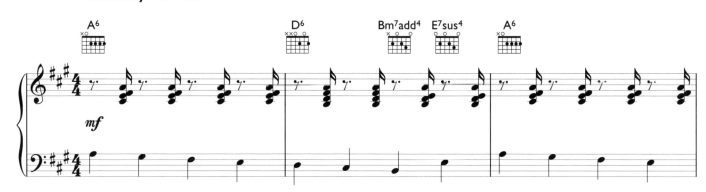

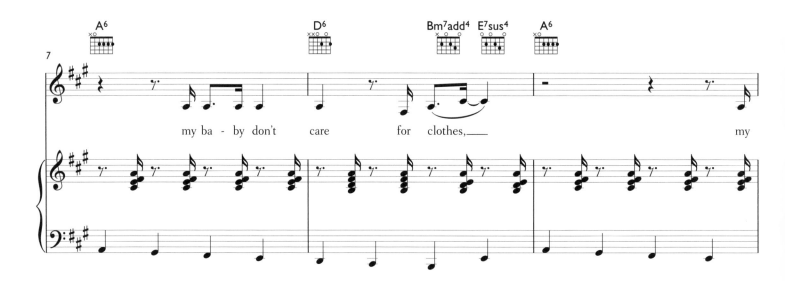

NOBODY'S FAULT BUT MINE

Traditional
Arranged by Nina Simone

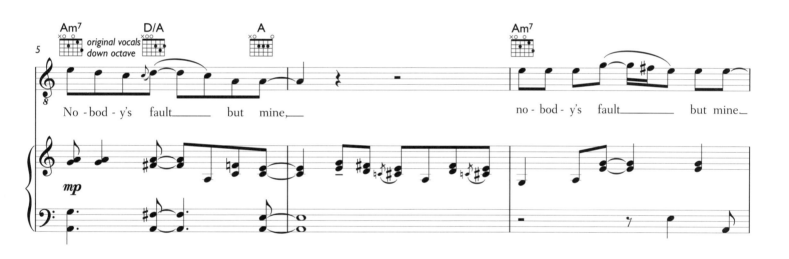

SINCE I FELL FOR YOU

Words and Music by Buddy Johnson

SINNERMAN

Words and Music by Nina Simone

Oh, sin-ner man, where__ he gon' run__ to?

78

TO BE YOUNG GIFTED AND BLACK

Words and Music by Nina Simone and Weldon Irvine

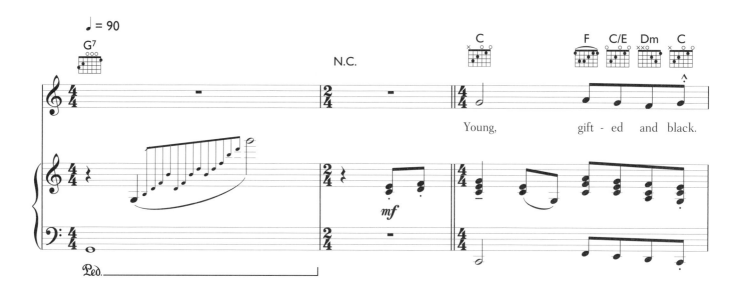

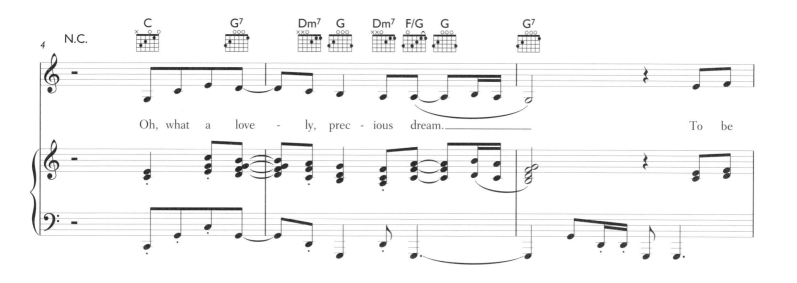

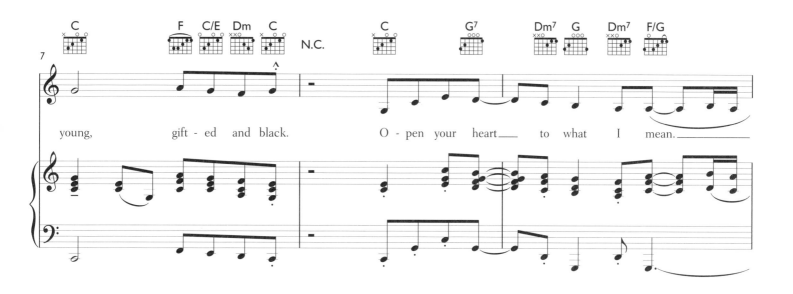

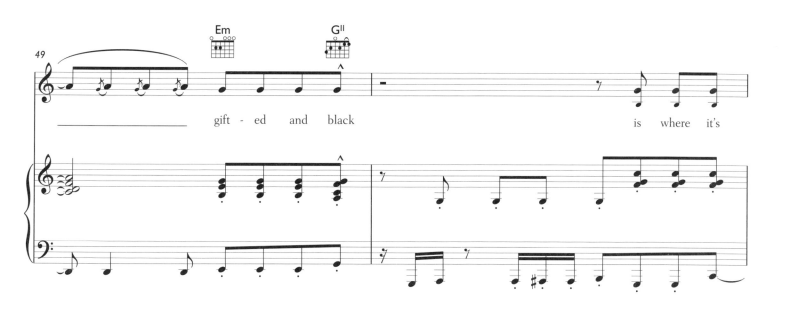

YOU'RE THE VOICE

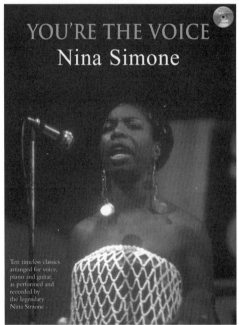

You're the Voice: Nina Simone (PVG)
ISBN: 0-571-52664-0
EAN13: 978-0-571-52664-2

Don't Let Me Be Misunderstood
Feeling Good
I Loves You Porgy
I Put A Spell On You
Love Me Or Leave Me
Mood Indigo
My Baby Just Cares For Me
Ne Me Quitte Pas (If You Go Away)
Nobody Knows You When You're Down And Out
Take Me To The Water

The outstanding vocal series from Faber Music
CD contains full backings for each song,
professionally arranged to recreate the sounds of the original recording